CLASSIC CO
DOT-TO-DOT
HORROR

D0189222

ILLUSTRATED BY GARETH MOORE

Connect the dots to create the stunning pictures in this book. There are 30 puzzles for you to complete – each one a masterpiece of vintage comic fun.

Instructions:

▷ Start at number 1, marked with a hollow dot, and then draw lines to each numbered dot in turn until you reach a hollow dot

▷ When you reach a hollow dot, take your pen off the page and move to the next number, which will also have a hollow dot. Then continue drawing lines from dot to dot

Hints and tips:

▷ If you aren't immediately sure which dot is attached to each number, look at the surrounding dots and numbers to work it out. Numbers are always directly above, below or to the side of a dot, or at one of the four main diagonals to it. They are never at any other position, and are always exactly the same distance away from the dot

▷ Number 1 is bolder than the other numbers, to help you find it more easily. The final number is bold too, so you know when you're finished

▷ Use a fine-tipped pen or pencil so that you don't obscure the dots and numbers you haven't yet used

▷ You don't have to start at number one – you can start anywhere you like and then fill in the bits you've missed out later

▷ Don't worry if you make a mistake – it's very unlikely that you'll be able to notice it once you have completed the final image, thanks to the intricate nature of each of the illustrations

▷ Once you have joined all the dots, why not try colouring in the pictures with pens or pencils?

▷ There is a small, finished version of each image at the back of the book

First published in Great Britain in 2016 by
Michael O'Mara Books Limited
9 Lion Yard
Tremadoc Road
London SW4 7NQ

Copyright © Michael O'Mara Books Limited 2016

All rights reserved. You may not copy, store, distribute, transmit, reproduce or otherwise make available this publication (or any part of it) in any form, or by any means (electronic, digital, optical, mechanical, photocopying, recording or otherwise), without the prior written permission of the publisher. Any person who does any unauthorized act in relation to this publication may be liable to criminal prosecution and civil claims for damages.

A CIP catalogue record for this book is available from the British Library.

Papers used by Michael O'Mara Books Limited are natural, recyclable products made from wood grown in sustainable forests. The manufacturing processes conform to the environmental regulations of the country of origin.

ISBN: 978-1-78243-727-7 in paperback print format

1 2 3 4 5 6 7 8 9 10

Cover designed by Jade Wheaton
Back cover images www.shutterstock.com

Printed and bound in Malta

www.mombooks.com
www.drgarethmoore.com

GHOSTLY TALES from the HAUNTED HOUSE

GHOSTLY TALES

CDC

12¢ MARCH

APPROVED BY THE COMICS CODE AUTHORITY

ENTER, MY FRIENDS...
COME WITH ME THROUGH
THE SHADOWS FROM
THE BEYOND...INTO
THE REALM OF THE
SUPERNATURAL...
IF YOU DARE!!

THE SNAKE THAT HELD A CITY CAPTIVE!

TALES OF TERROR

TALES OF HORROR

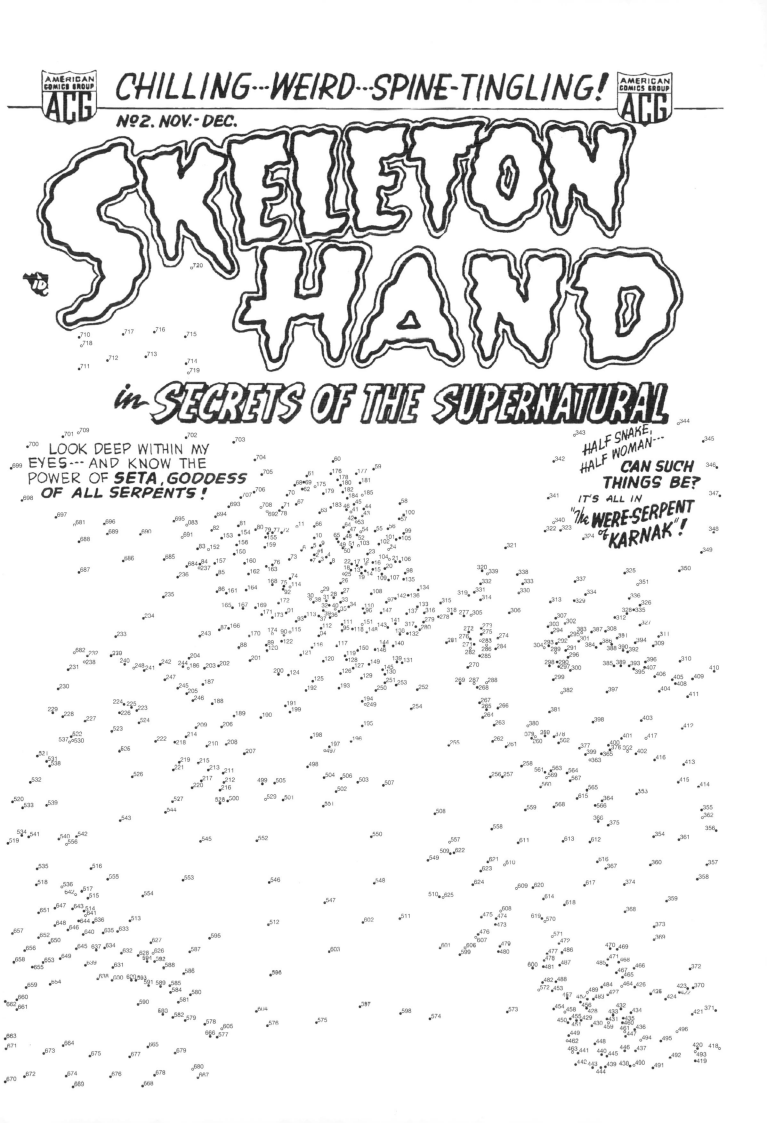

CHILLING---WEIRD---SPINE-TINGLING!

AMERICAN COMICS GROUP ACG

Nº 2. NOV.- DEC.

SKELETON HAND

in SECRETS OF THE SUPERNATURAL

LOOK DEEP WITHIN MY EYES--- AND KNOW THE POWER OF **SETA, GODDESS** OF ALL SERPENTS!

HALF SNAKE, HALF WOMAN--- CAN SUCH THINGS BE? IT'S ALL IN *"The WERE-SERPENT of KARNAK"!*

MAR. NO. 6
10¢

BEWARE!

I AM THE MUMMY
BRINGING YOU TALES CON-
JURED UP BY THE DEVIL
AND WRITTEN IN BLOOD!

TERROR

TALES

WEIRD! FANTASTIC! ASTOUNDING!

BAFFLING

MYSTERIES

MARCH 10c *Ace*

TERROR BENEATH THE TIDES

and other strange and exciting tales!

TALES OF THE SUPERNATURAL!

10c
No.3

WITCHCRAFT

The RED SPIDER

The GHOSTS' REVENGE

BETTER OFF DEAD

The 13th CLOWN

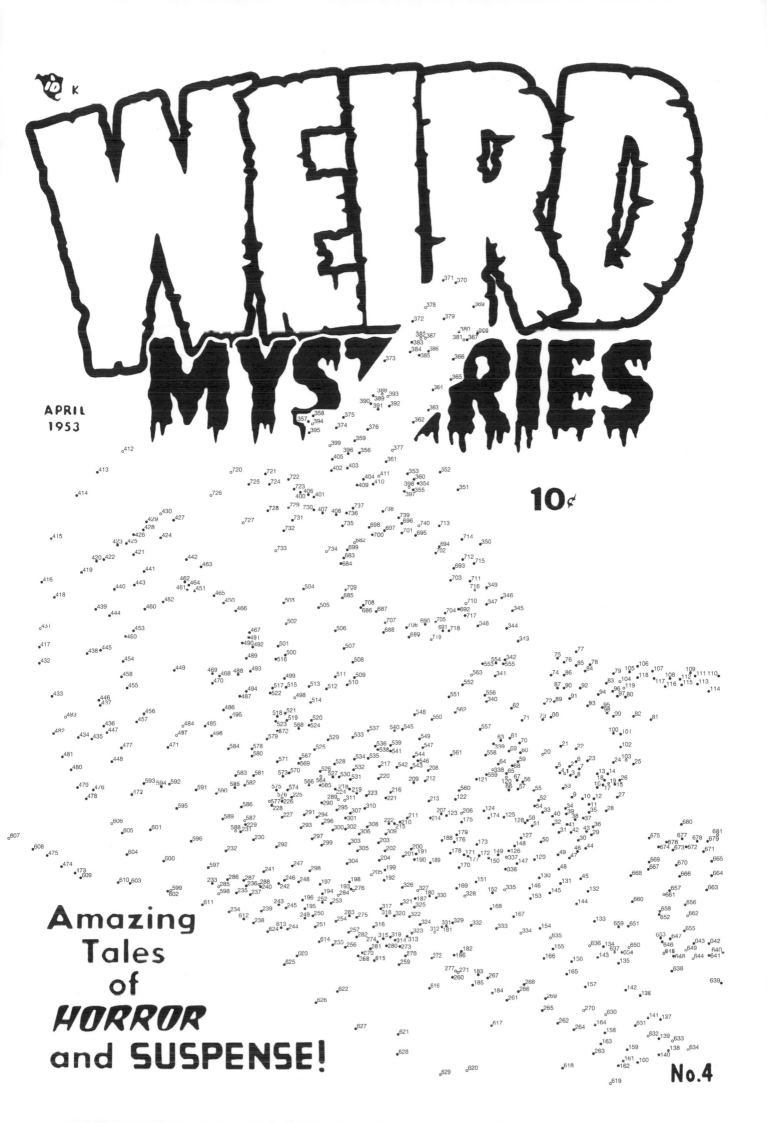

THE HAND OF FATE

FEB.
10¢

Ace

I WARNED YOU...THERE ARE
NO SHORT CUTS IN LIFE...NOW YOU
MUST **PAY** FOR YOUR FOLLY!

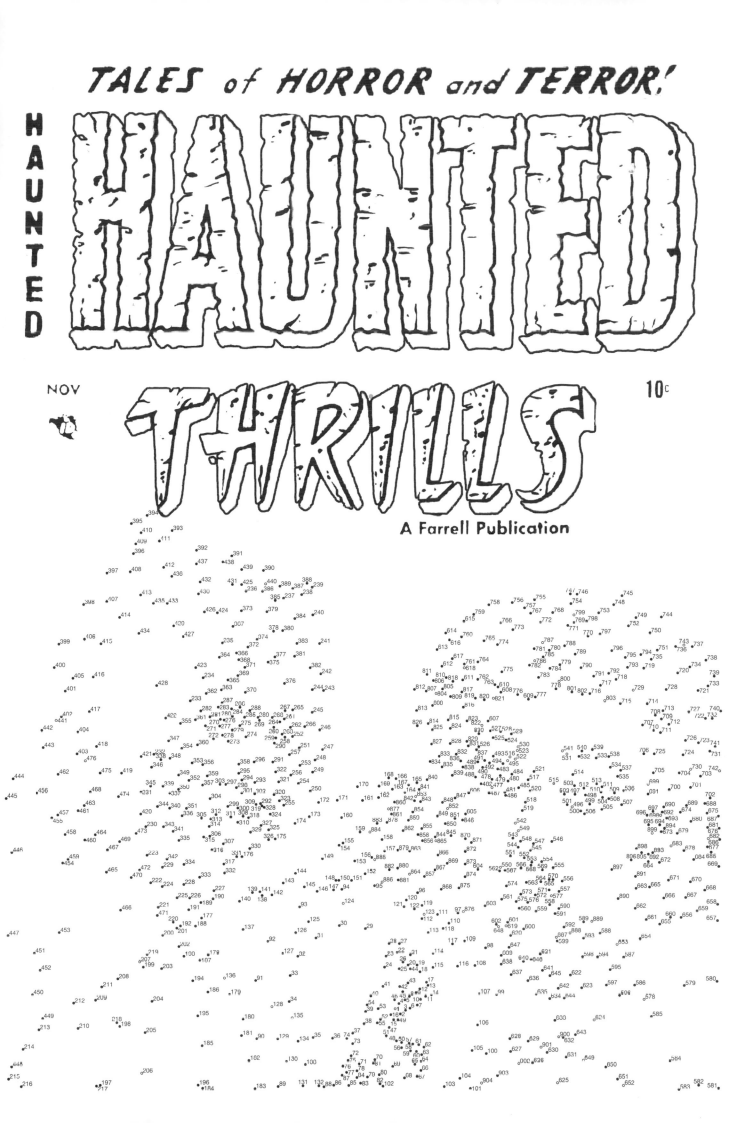

Jan No 3
WEIRD TERROR

GHOSTLY TALES OF SPINE-CHILLING HORROR

10c
K

AN AVON PUBLICATION

TALES OF FANTASY AND SUSPENSE!

No.3

ANC

10c

EERIE

Monster of the Storm!

The Case of the Painted Beasts!

The Mirror of Isis!

Was He Dead?

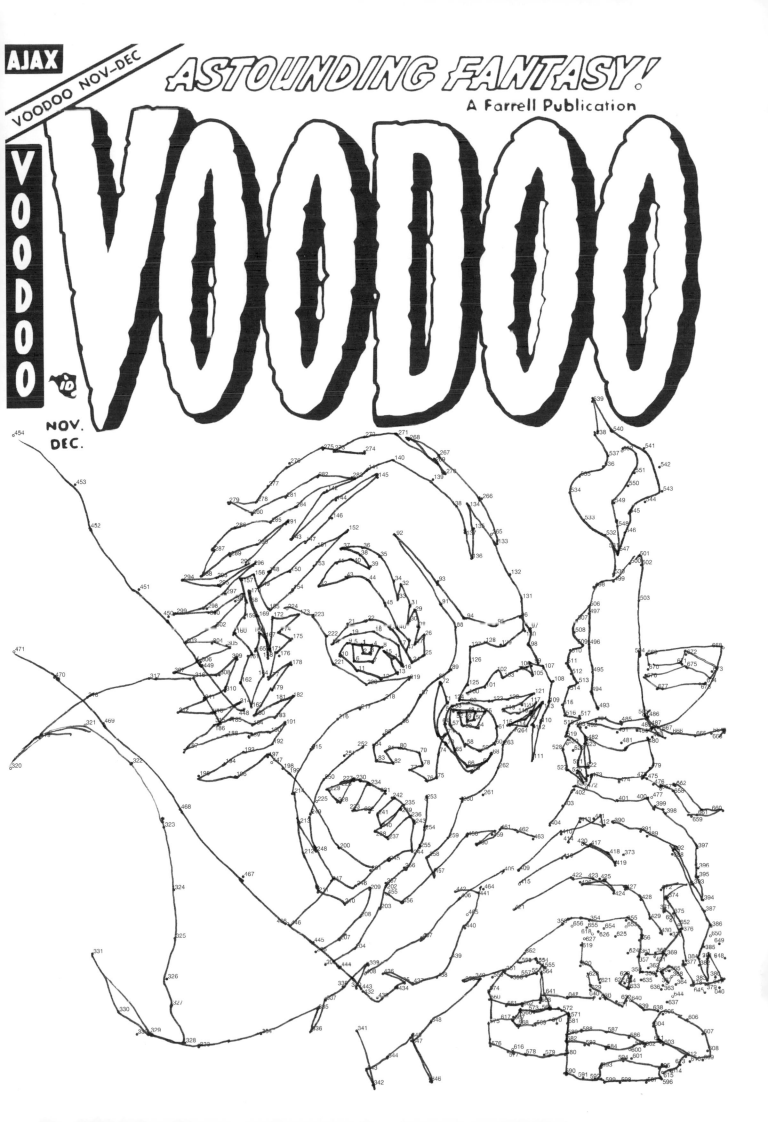

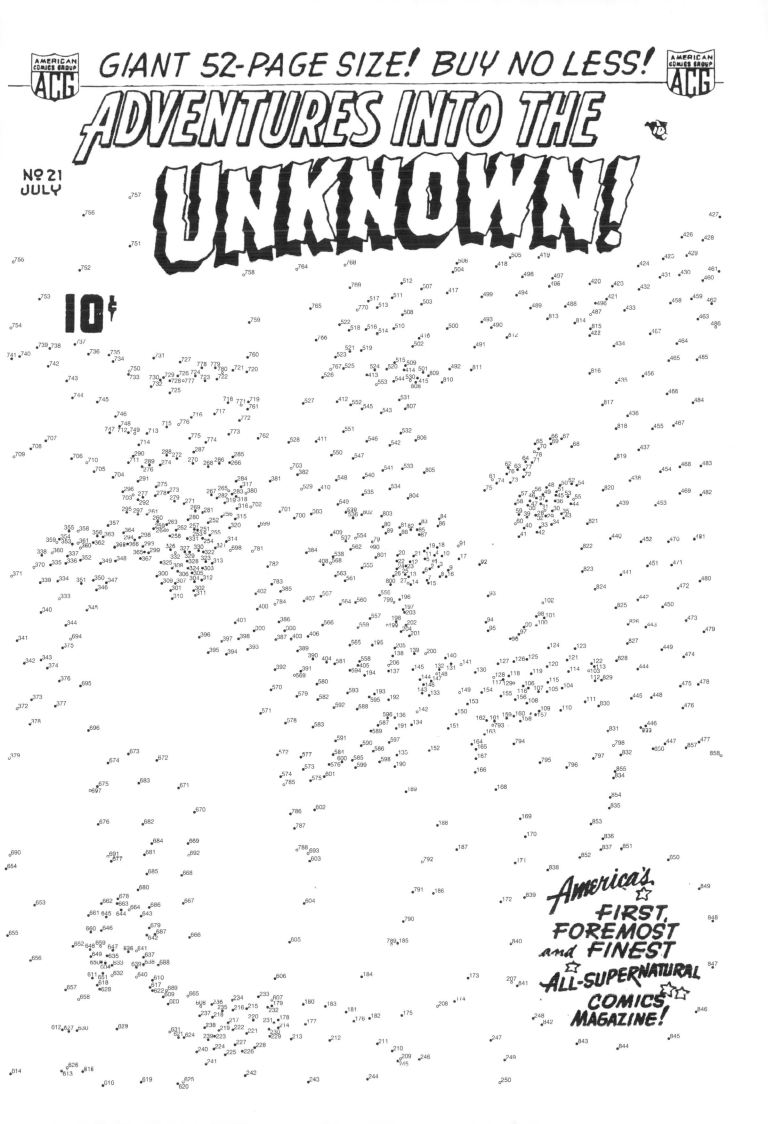

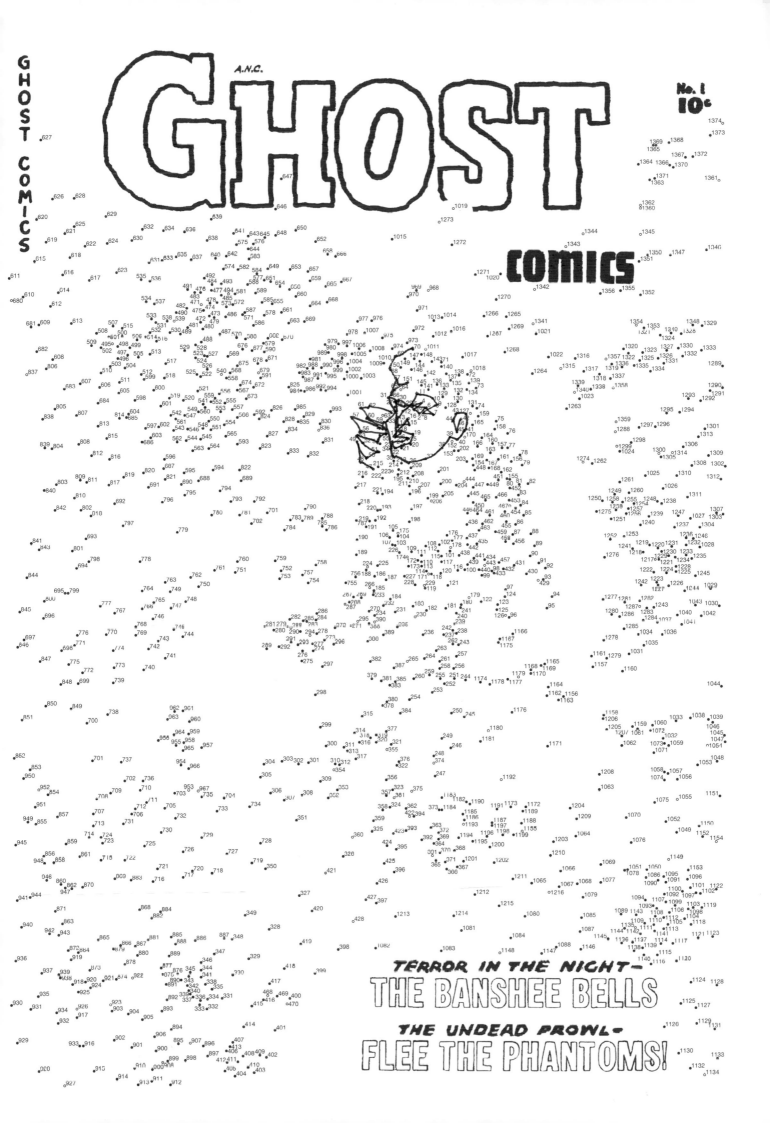

TALES OF HORROR IN OTHER WORLDS!

TOMB OF TERROR

No.15
MAY

10c

PDC

TOMB
OF TERROR

NEVER HAS A STORY BURST
WITH THE TERROR OF
BREAK-UP!

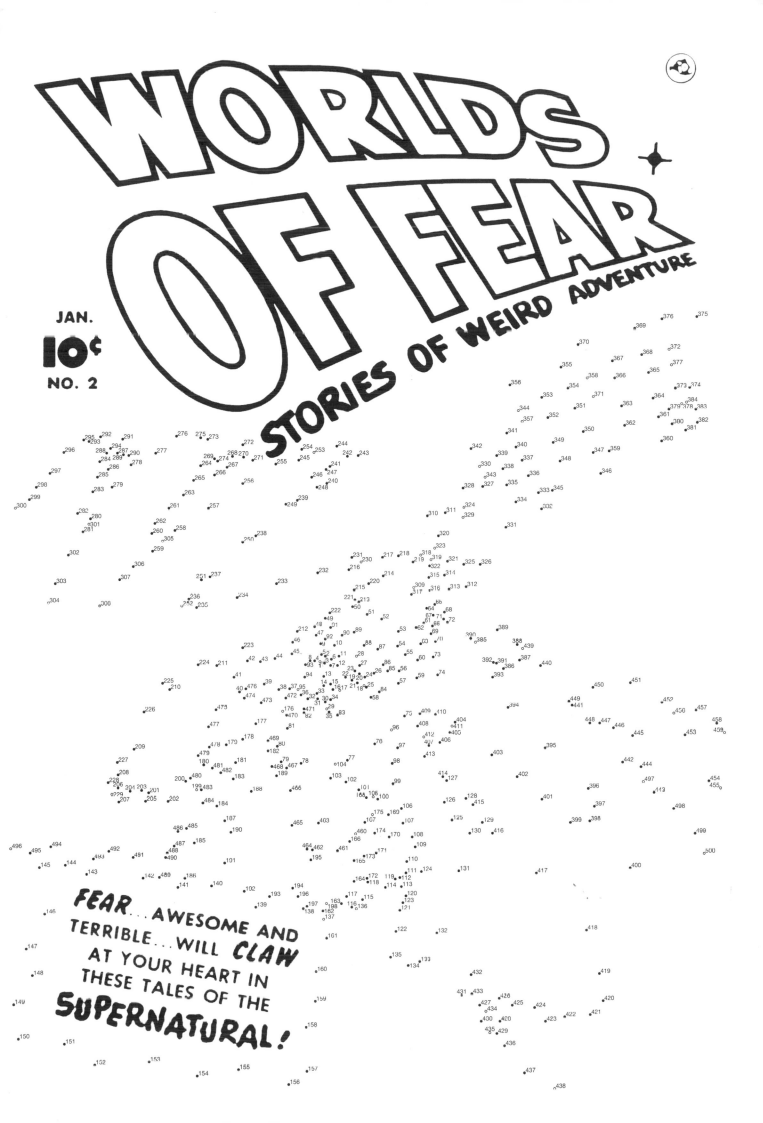

GHOSTLY

10¢ A N C NO. 123

WEIRD

STORIES

TRUDGING THROUGH THE STEAMING
FENS BY NIGHT, IT CAME, THIS LOATH-
SOME, DRIPPING FIGURE OF HORROR.
IN ITS WAKE, IT LEFT A TRAIL OF
DEATH AND DESTRUCTION. WHAT WAS
THIS TITANIC ENTITY FROM A WORLD
OF DARKNESS? ZEB BARLOW FOUND
OUT, BUT HE DID NOT LIVE TO IMPART
HIS DISCOVERY TO ANOTHER

The THING from The VOID

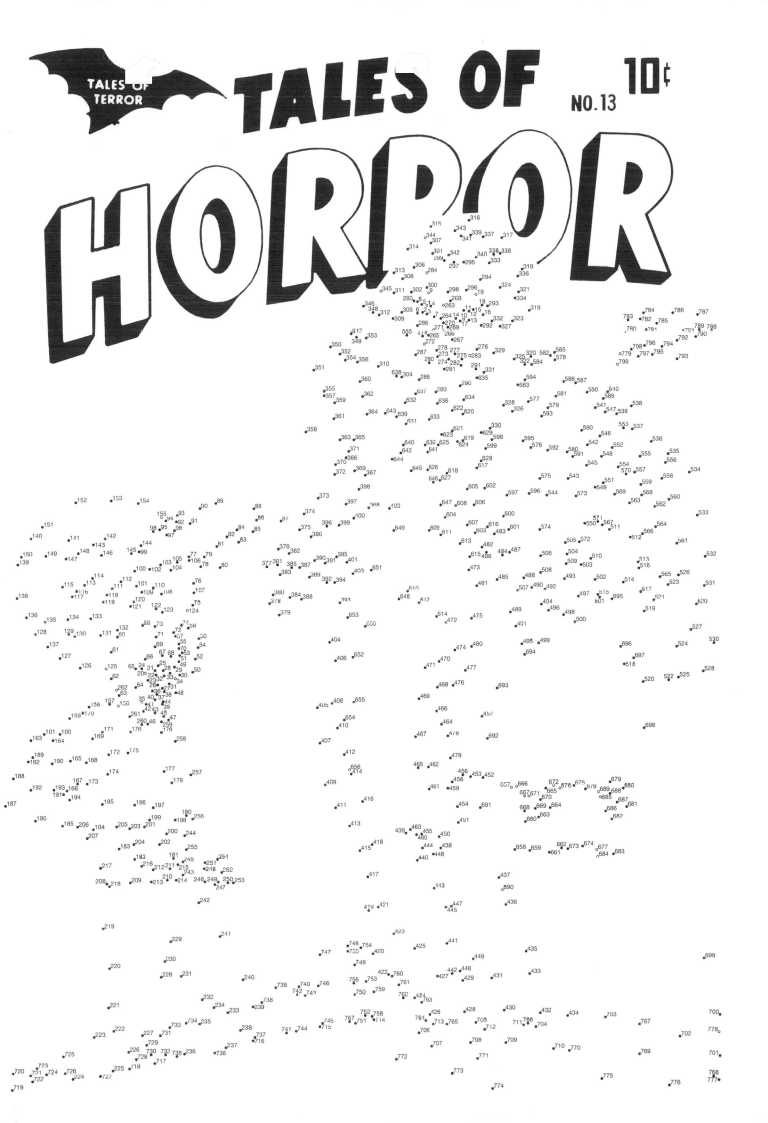

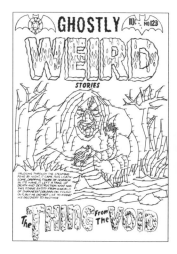

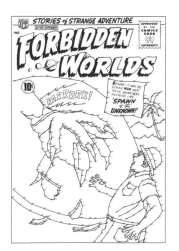